What if Bats has
and Spike has tw

Bats
Spike

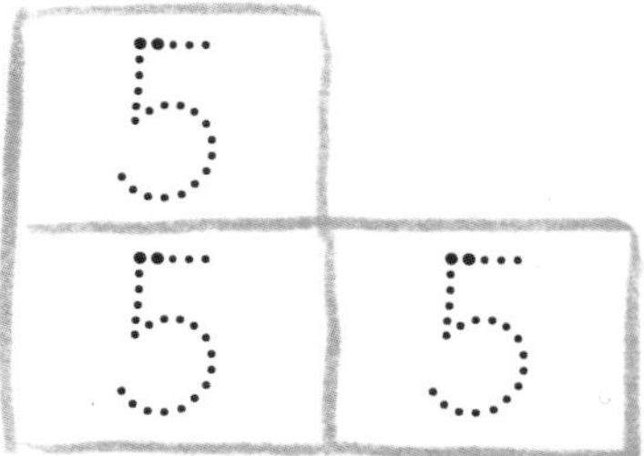

How many flowers do they have altogether?

What if Bats has 6 flowers and I have twice as many?

Bats
Spike

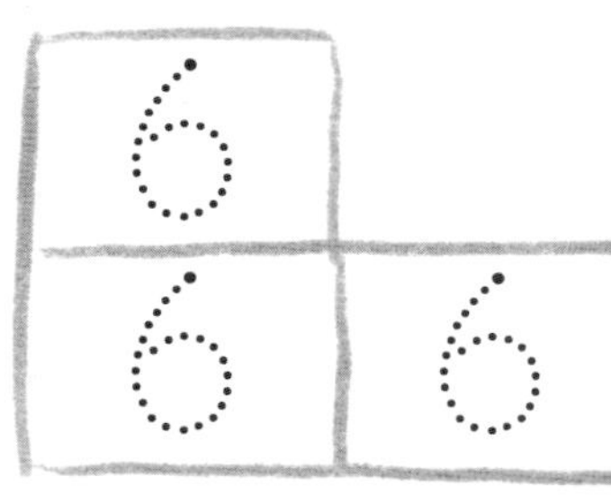

How many flowers do they have altogether?

Well done!

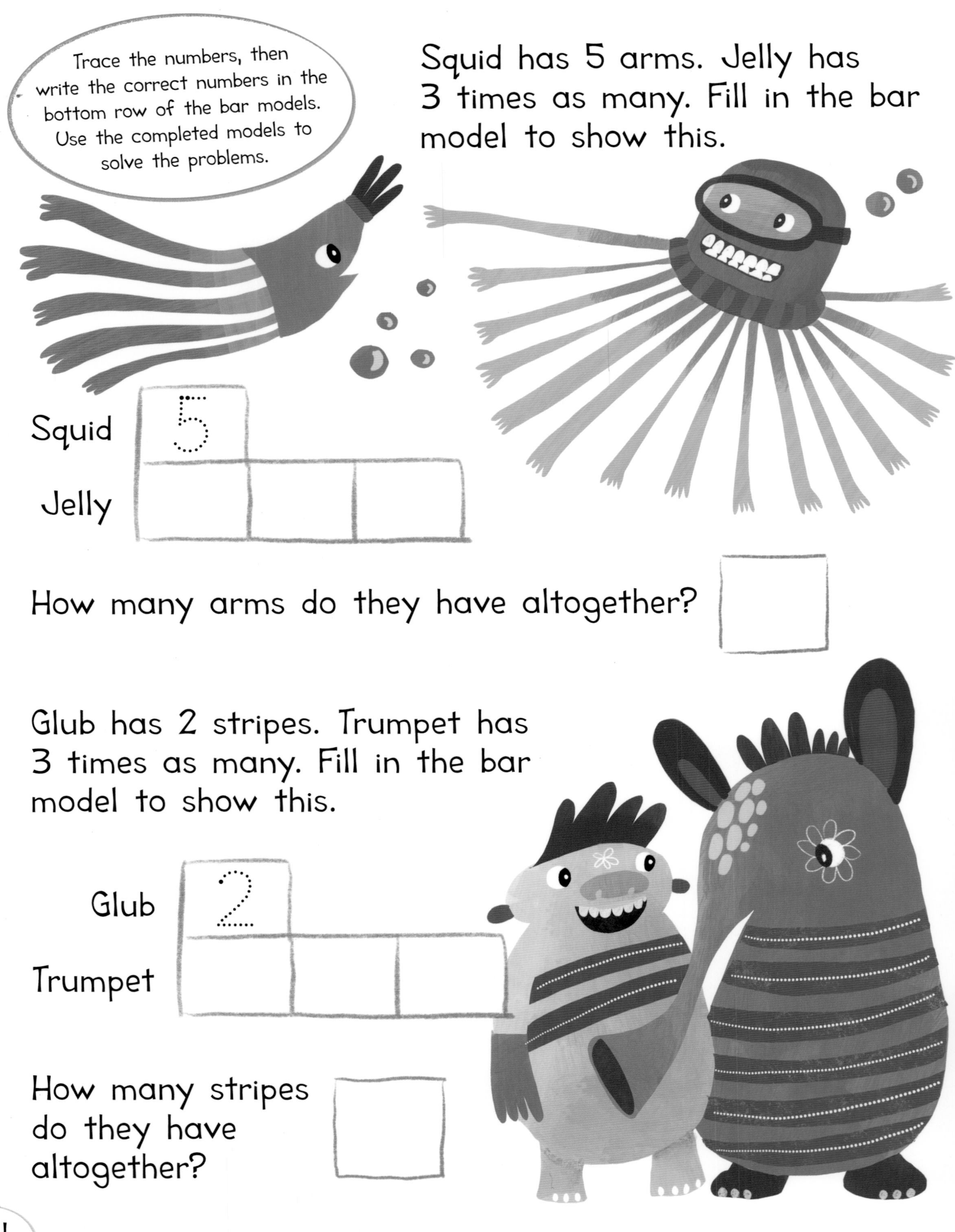

Trace the numbers, then write the correct numbers in the bottom row of the bar models. Use the completed models to solve the problems.

Squid has 5 arms. Jelly has 3 times as many. Fill in the bar model to show this.

Squid	5		
Jelly			

How many arms do they have altogether? ☐

Glub has 2 stripes. Trumpet has 3 times as many. Fill in the bar model to show this.

Glub	2		
Trumpet			

How many stripes do they have altogether? ☐

Scrute has 4 eyes.
Scope has 3 times
as many. Fill in
the bar model
to show this.

Scrute	4		
Scope			

How many eyes do they have altogether? ☐

Jot has 3 spots.
Smudge has
3 times as many.
Fill in the bar
model to show this.

Jot	3		
Smudge			

How many spots do
they have altogether? ☐

Well done!

Yum has 5 sweets. Scrump has 10 sweets. We can draw a bar model to show this.

Yum	Scrump
5	10
15	

How many sweets do they have altogether? ☐

What if Yum has 6 sweets?

Yum	Scrump
6	10

How many sweets do they have altogether? ☐

Fill in the blank bar model to help you solve the first problem on this page. Then wipe it clean and use it to help you solve the next problem.
Yum
Scrump
10
What if I have 7 sweets?
How many sweets do they have altogether?
Make up your own number of sweets that I might have, and solve the problem.
Yum has sweets.
How many sweets do they have altogether?
Well done!

Trace the dotted lines, then fill in the bar models. Use the completed models to solve the problems.

Splodge has 6 cans of paint. Splatter has 7 cans of paint.

We can draw a bar model to show how many they have altogether.

Splodge Splatter

How many cans of paint do they have altogether?

Doodle has 6 pencils. Scribble has 8 pencils.

Doodle Scribble

We can see that we need to add 6 and 8.

How many pencils do they have altogether?

Draw your own bar models and fill them in to show and solve the problems.
Smash has 6 blocks. Topple has 9 blocks.
Draw your bar model here
How many blocks do they have altogether?
Quiz has 6 books. Cram has 10 books.
Draw your bar model here
How many books do they have altogether?
Well done!

Trace the numbers, then write the correct numbers in the bottom row of the bar models. Use the completed models to solve the problems.

Lix ate 11 cakes. Bolt ate 6 cakes. We can draw a bar model to show how many *more* cakes Lix ate.

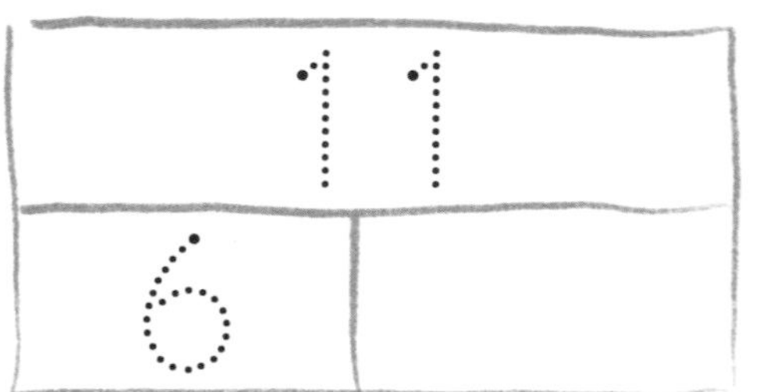

We need to find the difference between 11 and 6. Cross out 6 of these cakes to help you.

Lix ate ☐ more cakes.

What if most of the problem stays the same but Lix ate 12 cakes?

12	
6	

If you need help, draw 1 more cake in the group above, then cross out 6 to find the difference.

Lix ate ☐ more cakes.

Fill in the blank bar model to help you solve the first problem on this page. Then wipe it clean and use it to help you solve the next problem.
What if I eat 13 cakes?
Lix ate more cakes.
Make up your own number of cakes that Lix could have eaten. Solve the problem!
FLO
Lix ate cakes.
Lix ate more cakes.
Well done!

Trace the numbers and dotted lines, then fill in the bar models. Use the completed models to solve the problems.

Laze read 7 pages of her book. Splash read 5. We can draw a bar model to show how many *more* pages Laze read.

7	
5	

Laze read ☐ more pages.

Scoop built 8 sandcastles. Doug built 5 sandcastles.

Scoop built ☐ more sandcastles.

Fill in the blank bar model to help you solve the first problem on this page. Then wipe it clean and use it to help you solve the next problem.

Rocky ate 4 ice creams. Neo ate 2. How many more ice creams did Rocky eat?

What if I eat 5 ice creams?

Rocky ate ☐ more ice creams.

Make up your own number of ice creams that Rocky could have eaten. Solve the problem!

Rocky ate ☐ ice creams.

Rocky ate ☐ more ice creams.

Well done!

Draw your own bar models to show and solve the problems.

Hertz practised music for 9 minutes. Mono practised music for 5 minutes.

Draw your bar model here

How many more minutes did Hertz practise for?

Buzz spent 12 minutes playing music.
Patch spent 7 minutes playing music.

Draw your bar model here

How many more minutes did Buzz play for?

Tempo spent 10 minutes playing guitar.
Reverb spent 6 minutes playing guitar.

Draw your bar model here

How many more minutes did Tempo play for?

Buddy spent 15 minutes playing the drums.
Bird spent 2 minutes playing the saxophone.

Draw your bar model here

How many more minutes did Buddy play for?

Well done!

Trace the numbers, then write the correct numbers in the bottom row of the bar models. Use the completed models to solve the problems.

Swish scored 13 points. Dribble scored 5 *more* points than Swish. We can draw a bar model to show how many points Dribble scored.

13	5

Dribble scored ☐ points.

What if the problem stays the same, but Dribble scored 6 more points than Swish?

13	6

Dribble scored ☐ points.

Fill in the blank bar model to help you solve the first problem on this page. Then wipe it clean and use it to help you solve the next problem.
What if Dribble scored 7 more points than Swish?
13
Dribble scored points.
What if Dribble scored 8 more points than Swish?
Make up your own number of points more that Dribble could have scored. Solve the problem!
Dribble scored more points.
Dribble scored points.
Well done!

Trace the numbers and dotted lines, then write the correct numbers in the bottom row of the bar models. Use the completed models to solve the problems.

Zoom's car has 8 stripes. Zip's has 4 more.

Zoom's car has ☐ stripes.

Beep's car has 7 hearts. Axle's car has 2 more.

Axle's car has ☐ hearts.

Bump's car has 12 stars. Prang's has 3 more.

Prang's car has ☐ stars.

Spark's car has 9 spots. Trax's has 5 more.

Trax's car has ☐ spots.

Well done!

Draw your own bar models to show and solve these problems.

Grub has 8 carrots.
Fang has 6 more.

Draw your bar model here

Fang has  carrots.

Goop has 8 pineapples.
Pep has 7 more.

Draw your bar model here

Pep has ☐ pineapples.

Bar models can show several calculations at once. The pink bar model to the right shows us four.

7	3
10	

Subtraction is the inverse (opposite) of addition. Addition is the inverse of subtraction.

Addition is commutative – no matter which order we add two numbers, the sum is always the same.

7 + 3 = 10

3 + 7 = 10

10 – 3 = 7

10 – 7 = 3

We can count on from 12 to 18 or count back from 18 to 12 to find the missing number.

We can use bar models to solve missing number problems.

12	
18	

12 + ☐ = 18

Well done!

Fill in the bar models and find the missing numbers in these calculations.
20 - ☐ = 9
☐ + 9 = 17
☐ + 8 = 14